West of Boston

Verse by William Conelly

Illustrations by Nadia Kossman

Bumblebee Books
London

BUMBLEBEE PAPERBACK EDITION

Illustrated by Nadia Kossman

A CIP catalogue record for this title is
available from the British Library.

ISBN: 978-1-83934-115-1

Bumblebee Books is an imprint of
Olympia Publishers.

First Published in 2021

Bumblebee Books
Tallis House
2 Tallis Street
London
EC4Y 0AB

Printed in Great Britain

www.olympiapublishers.com

Dedication

for brother Tom

The Dashfield Pond

Tom pulled off both his shoes,
peeled out of both his socks
and splashed into the pond
to fish for magic rocks.

His mother read a book
two thoughtful strides away.
It told how raising hens
inspired thoughtful play.

A pebble charmed one shoe,
a cobble charmed the other,
Tom lugged a nobbled rock
uphill to charm his mother.

"I'll buy it for a hug."

"I'll sell it for a penny."

"Tommy, where're your socks?"

"Magicians don't wear any."

Hobby Hens

Tom’s mom adores her chickens,
Spool, Big Foot and Red.
She scatters kitchen scraps
around their makeshift shed.

Down the ramp they hustle,
a-scuffle over space,
clucking birdy ‘thank you’s’,
keen beaks on each keen face.

Tom wants an indoor hen.
He has an indoor cat,
but birds won't use the cat box.
Mom's not okay with that.

So Tommy balls some scraps
to heave across the glen.
"Big Foot will get them, Momma!
She's the speedy greedy hen!"

Garden Study

If I lean between roses,
when Mom's garden is wet
and dig with a teaspoon
I know what I'll get.

It won't be a beetle,
a mouse or a germ,
with three or four scoops
I'll turn up a worm,

a sluggish dirt sucker
the colour of ham,
bent on escaping
the place where I am,

S sucking one-way,
Z sucking back,
afraid I’m a chicken
in search of a snack.

Shopping Local

Tom bounds outdoors
across the street
fist full of pennies,
shoes full of feet.

Dad minds his steps
like his toes were sore.
It’s a woodland mile
to the town’s one store.

A blue car passes,
then a rust-trimmed truck.
Both drivers wave,
so that’s good luck.

ACK BEAR COUNTRY STORE
OPEN!

The store's near empty
most all Thursdays.
It fills up weekends
when a string band plays.

Tom hops indoors
and calls, "Hello!
I've come for a box
of orange mango!"

The clerk stops stocking.
"A strange banjo?
Or did you ask for
mange tallow?"

DASHFIELD
String Band!

"Orange-mango-passion
ALL-fruit, please!
I know you know!
And Dad wants cheese!"

"I remember you,"
the clerk man claims.
"You're the Dashfield lad
who likes word games.

"I'm mindful now.
Five pennies from you,
five dollars from Dad,
and the deal goes through."

The Short Hike Home

A shorter, steeper way leads from
the store toward young Tom's house.
Switchbacks beneath gigantic trees,
through shadows deep and solemn,
along side Black Bear Gutter Creek,
it's darkly, wholly awesome.

"The worry is," says Dad as he
starts down, "bears would like cheese
to picnic with beside their creek.
Keep an arm's reach of me.
Meet a black bear, we'll stop stock-still,
not start in fright and flee."

"Suppose I pour my all-fruit juice
on a rock for Mister Bear?
He'll want to lick, instead of chase.
We'll trick him into truce!"

"Maybe," says Dad, "but we *will* run
if we run across a moose."

NORTH

Toy Drawer

Tom keeps a brown brass key
inside one kitchen drawer.
His mom's forgotten now
what lock the key is for.

He keeps two much-used cars
as well, gifts from his aunt,
and sounds their thrum-thrum THRUMS!
since colour crayons can't.

He's dealt three game cards in,
the diamond kind with faces,
although the suit they ruled
has shuffled other places.

He's got four floppy discs,
from Dad's extinct computer,
paged through his treasures like
book chapters coloured pewter.

Five church sale creatures lurk
there too, or browse, or scurry,
and when all five are hidden,
cause Tom no end of worry.

“Your drawer’s a jungle,” Daddy says.
“Those church sale creatures hide
and sneak in order to survive.
Reach all around inside.”

Church elephant’s caught wading
through the rubber bands and string.
Tom catches Frog and Lion next.
They growl like anything.

Giraffe’s rear end gives him away,
it’s raised and pancake flat.
Tommy discovers Mud Mouse in
a tissue New Year’s hat.

Mom thinks another mother’s stove
has flattened poor Giraffe.
“Oh, no!” says Tommy growling.
“Frog ate the other half.”

Namesake

"So how did Mud Mouse get his name?"

"He fools around in puddles."

"He sits and plays some kind of game?"

"He likes the puddles' middles.
That's how he got sucked into a drain."

"A drain in a puddle's middle?"

"Daddy, his body bent into a sprain.
He couldn't kick or wiggle.
I had to grab him out again,
choking, trying to giggle."

"Mud covered, I suppose."

"He's got no drain-proof clothes!
Mud on his back, mud on his middle,
mud snuffled up his nose!"

"So that's how Mud Mouse got his name."

"Yes, Daddy, I suppose."

Sweet Dreams

Lullaby Tomkins,
bed clothes piled deep,
lost little visions
turning to sleep,

visions of Kitty,
a clucky red hen,
the ocean of sunlight
ebbing again.

Wake up tomorrow,
wake up and call
until Mommy answers
out in the hall,

singing her answers
from a new day,
singing the moon
has melted away.

Lantern Shades

Suppose the moon was lemon candy,
hung from a tree limb, sweet and yellow,
a willow tree limb, two trees south.

Suppose you were a wakeful fellow,
who always kept a fish net handy,
because he fished around the house,

and didn't mind a late walk south
on nights the light was tinted yellow
with lantern shades of lemon candy.

Suppose your kitty’s name was Brandy
and came along to hunt Mud Mouse.
Suppose the grass felt damp as Jell-O,

and even it was tinted yellow,
as you stood tiptoe, two trees south,
and netted all that lemon candy.

Suppose in bed it looked so mellow,
so lantern-tinted lemon dandy,
you let the moon melt in your mouth.

Counting

How many soap bubbles to
tickle your nose?

One is good fun,
twenty's too many.

How many pinecones to
cover your toes?

If steadied a while,
quite a large pile.
With pine sap for glue,
a bare tacky two.

How many washcloths to
wrap up your head?

Dry ones keep slipping.
Three if they're dripping.

How many stuffed creatures
to tuck in your bed?

Frog and Lion always roar,
so a sheepish, drowsy troupe
of four.

How many feathers
in a proper bunch?

A chicken full if
they're alive,
otherwise I think five.

How many nibbles
make up your lunch?

Six carrot sticks,
six sticks of cheese,
six crispy apples
in apple juice, please!

How many cars thrum down your street?

Seven dark and seven light,
some from the left, some from the right,
dark in daytime, lit at night.

How many footprints follow your feet?

Crunching leaves an autumn day?
I can’t possibly say.
Overlooking trampled snow?
Eight hundred or so.

Clean

Tommy's in the bathtub,
Daddy's in the shower,
Daddy for a minute,
Tommy for an hour.

Daddy's got a scratchy cloth
and special soap for grease.
Tom's got a whale-shaped sponge,
in water it's obese.

Daddy needs to rush.
Tom would rather not.
Daddy's off for Greenfield,
flushed and dripping hot,

while Tommy slip-n-slides
around the empty tub,
slewing like an otter,
singing rub-a-dub!

All Done

I ate my sandwich down to scraps.
Now cat and I can go for naps.

Jam this half-peach back on its tree,
the rest has made a mess of me.

And pour my milk back in the cow.
It’s really hers. I’m fed up now.

Unpuzzled

Across the hills and forest,
to the white fringe of the sea,
are any other creatures
quite the same as me?

My mother will say, “No.”
The cat could not care less.
Chickens don’t suppose,
but Father tells me, “Yes.”

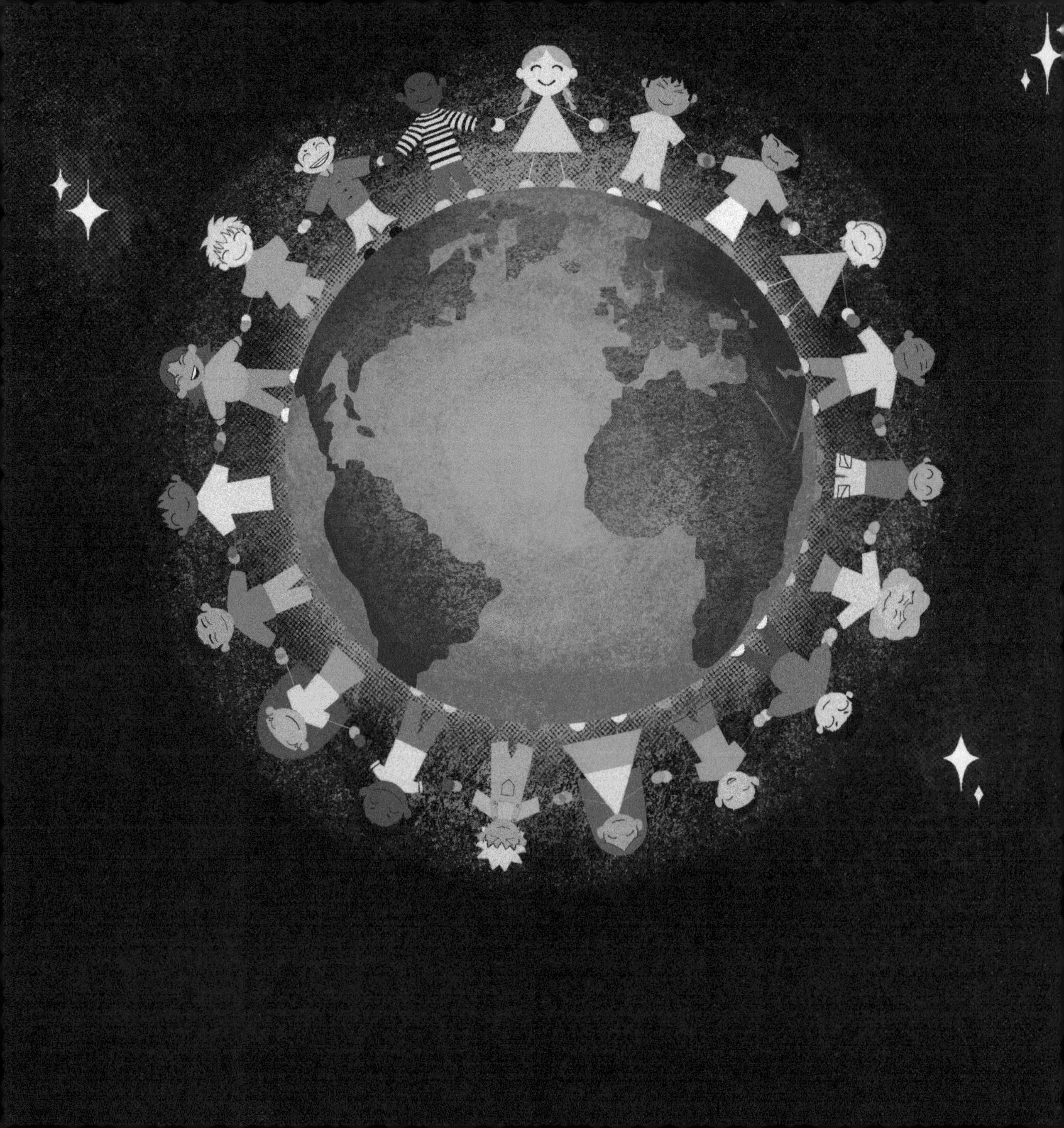

"All across the wide world,
breathing plenteous air,
learning love and laughter,
almost everywhere,

"children the same as you
wake up from sleep and think.
Every little person's life
must somehow interlink."

My mother smiles and says,
"Computers make that true,
but Tom nobody anywhere
is quite completely you."

I know what they both mean.
Whoever and what I see,
wherever in the wide world,
I’m only always me.

Afterwards

Can you recollect a bubble
once the bubble pops?
Can you recollect a poem
once the reading stops?

About the Author

William Conelly grew up in a family of four boys and, once married, had three boys himself. Joined to an education in English verse, he is well-suited to create a lyric boyhood in a woodland township, a township very like the one his family enjoyed more than twenty years, West of Boston.

About the Illustrator

Nadia Kossman is an illustrator from Queens, New York. She is inspired by the fairy tales, mid century cartoons and bright colors. When she is not drawing she is usually out on a walk to find interesting trees, south of Boston.

CPSIA information can be obtained
at www.ICGtesting.com
Printed in the USA
LVHW071509300421
686094LV00008B/439